# Time Pieces

## for
## B flat Saxophone

Music through the Ages in Two Volumes

### Volume 1

Selected and arranged by
Ian Denley

The Associated Board of
the Royal Schools of Music

# CONTENTS

# Time Pieces for B flat Saxophone

## Volume 1

*for Gordon Lewin*

## *c.*1500  A Romp

Anon.

(based on an English folksong)

## *c.*1550  The Rune of the Weaver

Anon.
Traditional Scottish

AB 2768

# *c.*1585  A Plain Song

Anon.

(based on a medieval chant)

# 1600  Fine Knacks for Ladies

John Dowland
(1563–1626)

from *Second Book of Songs or Ayres*

## 1609    In Sherwood livde stout Robin Hood

from *Fourth Booke of Ayres*

Robert Jones
(fl. 1597–1615)

## 1684    Bois épais

from *Amadis*, Op. 63

Jean-Baptiste Lully
(1632–1687)

In translation, this title is usually 'Lonely Woods' or 'Sombre Woods'.

## *c.*1710 Bourrée

from *English Suite No. 2*, BWV 807

Johann Sebastian Bach
(1685–1750)

## 1784 Marche funèbre del Signor Maestro Contrapunto

K. 453a

Wolfgang Amadeus Mozart
(1756–1791)

## 1793 Minuet
from *12 German Dances*, Hob. IX/10

Joseph Haydn
(1732–1809)

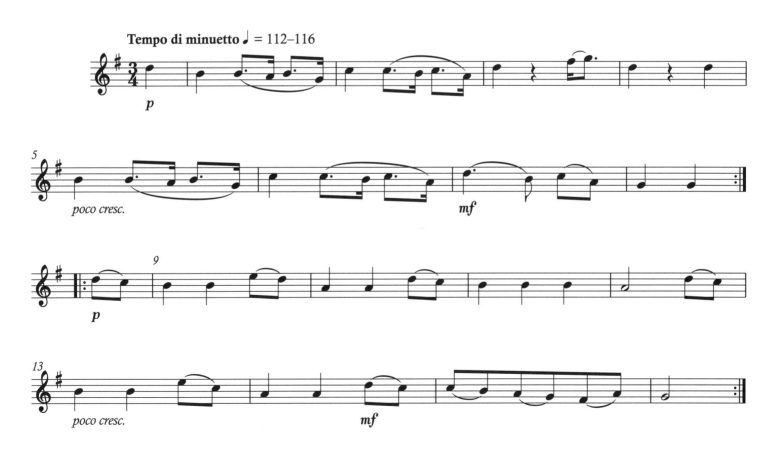

## 1832 Romance

from *L'elisir d'amore*

Gaetano Donizetti
(1797–1848)

## 1834 Serenade

from *Harold in Italy*, Op. 16

Hector Berlioz
(1803–1869)

AB 2768

# 1848  **The Merry Peasant**

from *Album for the Young*, Op. 68

Robert Schumann
(1810–1856)

1892

# Grandfather's Dance

from *The Nutcracker*, Op. 71

Pyotr Tchaikovsky
(1840–1893)

'Grandfather's' tempo ♩ = 144–152

# 1899 Prélude

from *Jack in the Box*

Eric Satie
(1866–1925)

Lively and spiky ♩ = 120–126

## 1901    Linden Lea

Ralph Vaughan Williams
(1872–1958)

## 1931   The Joker

from *In aller Frühe*, Op. 126b

Aleksandr Grechaninov
(1864–1956)

## 1946   My Horse has Cast a Shoe

from *Pacific 1860*

Noël Coward
(1899–1973)

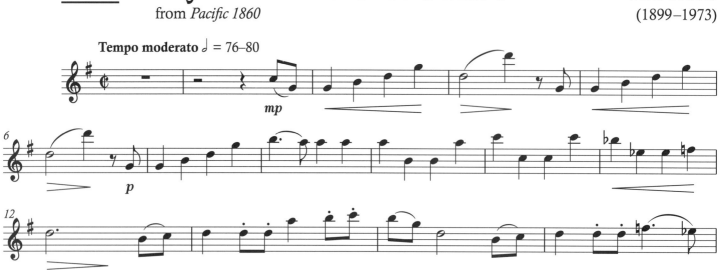

## 1952 On the Hills

from *In Ireland*

Marjorie Corker

# 1972    A Christmas Tune

Gordon Jacob
(1895–1984)

# 1987    Promenade
from *Simple Suite No. 3*

John Reeman
(b.1946)

Printed in England by Caligraving Ltd, Thetford, Norfolk

Music origination by
Barnes Music Engraving Ltd, East Sussex

     AB 2768      10:08

# Time Pieces for B flat Saxophone

## Volume 1

*for Gordon Lewin*

### c.1500  A Romp
(based on an English folksong)

Anon.

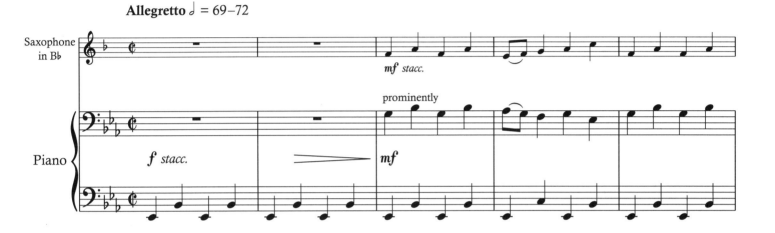

AB 2768

## *c.*1550 **The Rune of the Weaver**

Anon.
Traditional Scottish

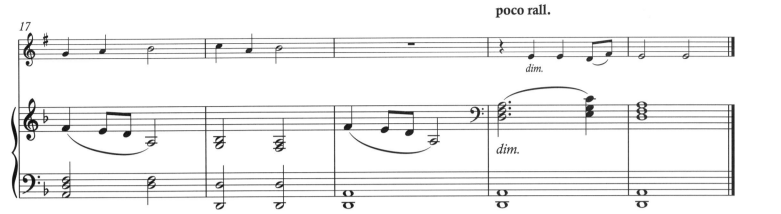

## c.1585 A Plain Song

(based on a medieval chant)

Anon.

# 1600 Fine Knacks for Ladies

John Dowland
(1563–1626)

from *Second Book of Songs or Ayres*

AB 2768

# 1609 In Sherwood livde stout Robin Hood

from *Fourth Booke of Ayres*

Robert Jones
(fl. 1597–1615)

## 1684 **Bois épais**

from *Amadis*, Op. 63

Jean-Baptiste Lully
(1632–1687)

In translation, this title is usually 'Lonely Woods' or 'Sombre Woods'.

AB 2768

poco rall.

# *c.*1710 **Bourrée 2**

from *English Suite No. 2*, BWV 807

Johann Sebastian Bach
(1685–1750)

## 1784 Marche funèbre del Signor Maestro Contrapunto

K. 453a

Wolfgang Amadeus Mozart
(1756–1791)

# 1793 **Minuet**

from *12 German Dances*, Hob. IX/10

Joseph Haydn
(1732–1809)

# 1832 Romance

from *L'elisir d'amore*

Gaetano Donizetti
(1797–1848)

# 1834 Serenade

from *Harold in Italy*, Op. 16

Hector Berlioz
(1803–1869)

## 1848    **The Merry Peasant**

from *Album for the Young*, Op. 68

Robert Schumann
(1810–1856)

# 1892   Grandfather's Dance

Pyotr Tchaikovsky
(1840–1893)

from *The Nutcracker*, Op. 71

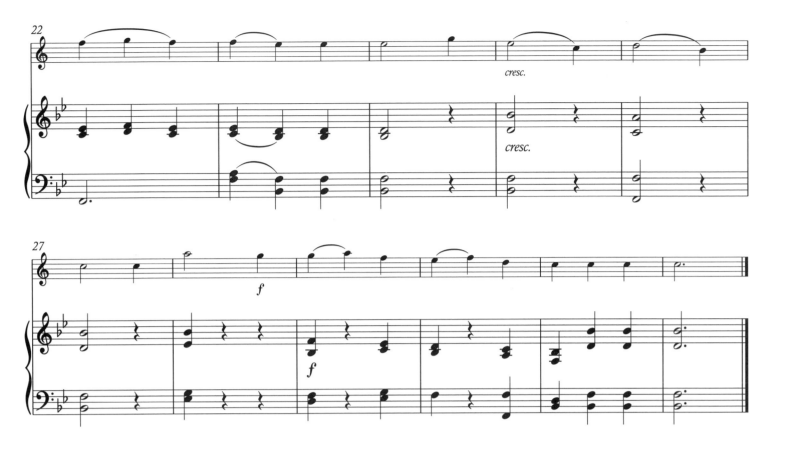

## 1899 Prélude

from *Jack in the Box*

Eric Satie
(1866–1925)

# 1901 Linden Lea

Ralph Vaughan Williams
(1872–1958)

# 1931 The Joker

from *In aller Frühe*, Op. 126b

Aleksandr Grechaninov
(1864–1956)

# 1946    My Horse has Cast a Shoe

from *Pacific 1860*

Noël Coward
(1899–1973)

# 1952 On the Hills

from *In Ireland*

Marjorie Corker

**Andante tranquillo** ♩ = *c*.96

AB 2768

# 1972    A Christmas Tune

Gordon Jacob
(1895–1984)

# 1987 Promenade

from *Simple Suite No. 3*

John Reeman
(b. 1946)

Music origination by
Barnes Music Engraving Ltd, East Sussex
Printed in England by Caligraving Ltd, Thetford, Norfolk

10:08

AB 2768